How to be a BUG WARRIOR

Little
Steps
PUBLISHING

Published in the United Kingdom in 2020
by Little Steps Publishing
Uncommon, 126 New King's Road,
London SW6 4LZ
www.littlestepspublishing.co.uk

Text copyright © 2020 The Parent-Child Dino Research Team
Illustrations copyright © 2020 Loyal Kids
Adapted and written by Stephanie Stahl
Designed by Verity Clark

A CIP record for this book is available from the British Library.

ISBN: 978-1-912678-25-9

Printed in China

10 9 8 7 6 5 4 3 2 1

How to be a BUG WARRIOR

Illustrated by Loyal Kids

Danny Dino and his friends were upset,
they really wanted to go to the park.
After all, everyone else was going.

'Many people in Dinoville
have been feeling ill,' said
Danny Dino's mum, 'if you
want to play outside, you
need to wear a mask.'

'I don't want to wear a mask,' Danny Dino complained. 'It looks so silly!'

That afternoon, the dino friends trotted happily to the park. Everyone was wearing a mask, except Danny Dino!

'It's so uncomfortable,'
he said. 'I can't breathe!'

Suddenly their friend Leila Dino walked past.

'Achooo!'

'I'm sorry!' she said, scratching her head.

'That was a super sneeze!' Danny Dino giggled.

When Danny Dino came home from the park, he felt very hungry. His tummy rumbled. Grrrrrrr!

Mummy Dino had baked his favourite treat: double chocolate muffins. Yum!

His friends went to wash their hands but Danny Dino could not wait. He picked up a cake and shuffled it right into his mouth. 'Delicious!' he beamed.

A few days later, Danny Dino started feeling a little dizzy and he couldn't stop sneezing.

Then he became feverish and had a sore throat.
'I'm feeling under the weather!' he sighed,
climbing into bed.

Doctor Pterosaur came right away to see how he could help.
He asked Danny Dino if he'd gone out.
'Hmm, I went to the park the other day,' said Danny Dino.
'I saw Leila Dino and she sneezed on me!'
'Did you wear a mask?' asked the doctor, 'it's important
to do so.'
'I had one but it felt uncomfortable so
I took it off,' Danny Dino explained.

Mummy Dino looked worried while Doctor Pterosaur listened to Danny Dino's breathing.
'He has a bad flu!' the doctor said. 'He needs to stay in bed and rest.'

A couple of days later, Dr Pterosaur and Danny Dino's friends came to check on him. He was feeling a little better.

'Why did we not get ill?' asked Molly Dino.

'You all wore masks,' explained Dr Pterosaur, 'and they blocked the virus.'

'Danny Dino ate a muffin but he did not wash his hands first,' said Molly Dino.

'That's probably how he got ill,' said Dr Pterosaur. 'If you don't wash your hands, the virus can go inside your body, without you even noticing it.'

'When Leila Dino sneezed, she wasn't wearing a mask.

She didn't have any tissues either,' said Molly Dino.

'She should have sneezed into her elbow to prevent the virus from spreading,' said Dr Pterosaur.

'Leila Dino wasn't careful at all!' said Molly.

'If you sneeze, you should cover your nose with a tissue, then throw it into the bin,' explained Dr Pterosaur. 'Make sure you always wash your hands afterwards,'

'Here is my seven-step super handwash for when you come home,

1. 'Scrub the inside

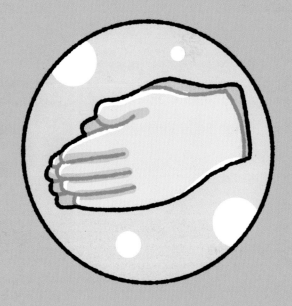

2. and then the back of your hands.

3. Interlace your fingers

4. and clean the back of your fingers too.

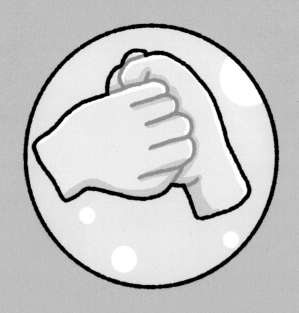

before eating or after using the bathroom,' said Dr Pterosaur.

5. Wash your thumbs,

6. your fingernails

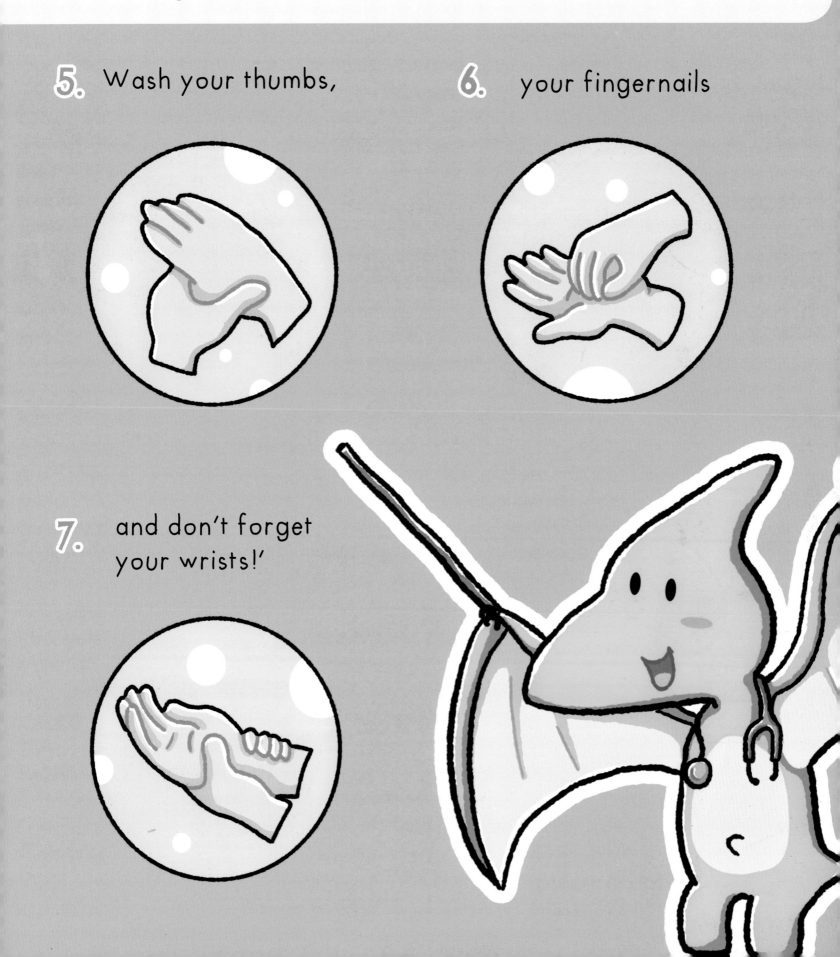

7. and don't forget your wrists!'

One week later, Danny Dino felt much better. 'I won't forget Dr Pterosaur's advice on how to wash my hands for twenty seconds, and be mindful of others so we can sweep these mean viruses away!'

Do you know what viruses are?

They are tiny creatures that you can't touch or see unless you have a microscope. Several families of viruses exist such as the flu. You might have also heard of the Coronavirus or Covid-19 that made many people sick all around the world.

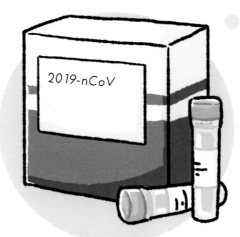

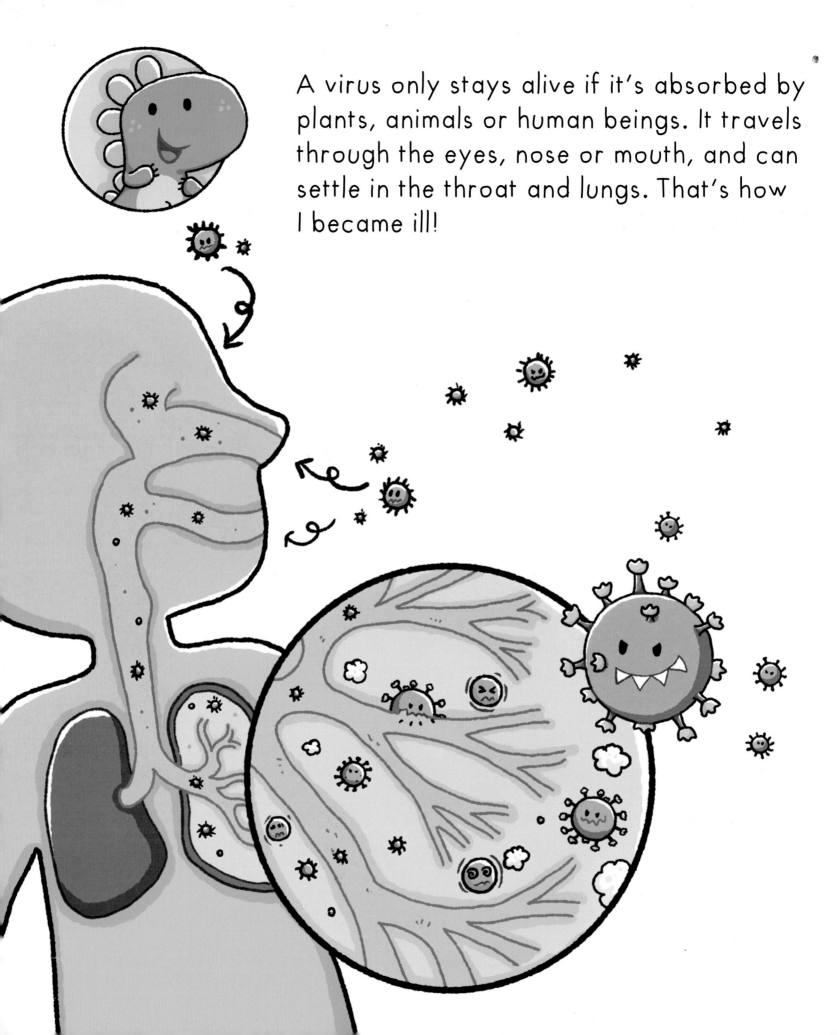

A virus only stays alive if it's absorbed by plants, animals or human beings. It travels through the eyes, nose or mouth, and can settle in the throat and lungs. That's how I became ill!

First you might have a mild cough and feel feverish. Sometimes your breathing could become more difficult too. Make sure you speak to or see your doctor right away.

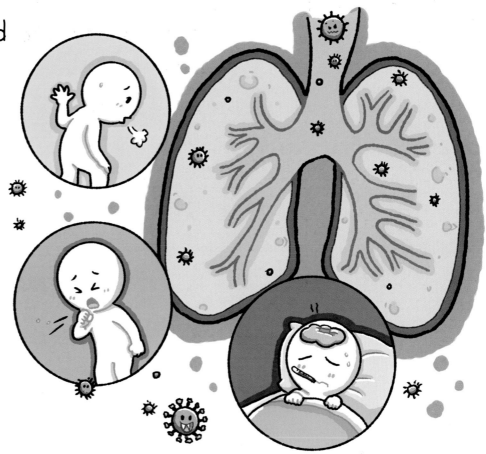

When people don't feel well, they should not meet up with their friends. That's how they can prevent the virus from spreading around them.

Now that you have read my book,

Quiz

1. What should you do when you sneeze in a public place? (10 points)

a. Cough hard so you get rid of the virus.

b. Cover your nose with your hands.

c. Cover your nose with a tissue or sneeze into your elbow.

2. What is the first thing you should do when you get home? (10 points)

a. Hug your mum and dad.

b. Wash your hands with soap for twenty seconds.

c. NO need to wash your hands, eat a snack right away.

3. Do you remember the order of Dr Pterosaur's seven-step method on how to wash your hands? (10 points)

a. Back of hands, inside of hands, fingers interlaced, back of fingers, fingernails, thumbs and wrists.

b. Inside of hands, back of hands, fingers interlaced, back of fingers, thumbs, fingernails and wrists.

c. Inside of hands, back of hands, fingers interlaced, pull the hands, back of fingers, base of index and wrists.

4. How should you wear a mask? (10 points)

a. Wear at least two or three masks at the same time.

b. Masks can be worn upside down too.

c. Wear your mask tightly on your face, covering your nose, mouth and chin.

5. If you are feeling sick, what should you do? (10 points)

a. Stay home and call your doctor to seek advice.

b. Invite your friends to your house and have a party.

c. Meet up with your friends, they will make you feel better.

Check your score!

40-50 points: Congratulations, you are bug warrior! You have learnt how to protect yourself and others in order to stay away from viruses. Share your knowledge!

30-40 points: You are awesome, you know a lot of things about viruses but you are missing some key facts. Read this book again and retake the quiz to see if you score higher.

Under 30 points: You know some of the basic steps on how to tackle viruses but if you want to become a bug warrior, go through this book again.

Answers: 1.c 2.b 3.b 4.c 5.a

Here are my 6 tips on how to protect yourself and the people around you!

1 Wash your hands with soap often and count to twenty to make sure you scrub thoroughly.

2 Stay home if you are not feeling well.

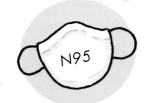

3 If you have to go out, wear a mask so you don't share your germs.

4 Take the medications given by your doctor and rest.

5 To help your body fight the bug, drink enough water and eat healthy by having plenty of fruits and vegetables.

6 A vaccine is the best way to prevent you from becoming ill. The doctor will inject a small amount of liquid into your arm. Don't be scared, it only lasts a few seconds and it's not painful at all.